UNDERSTANDING COMMERCIAL ICE MAKERS

Harry Parker

BNP Business News Publishing Company
Troy, Michigan

18324220

4-90

Administrative Editor: Phillip R. Roman
Cover Illustration: Renée Parker
Editor: Nancy Marcetti

Library of Congress Cataloging in Publication Data

Parker, Harry, 1955—
    Understanding commercial ice makers.

    Includes index.
    1. Ice—Manufacture. I. Title.
TP492.7.P37   1988   621.5'8   88-24095

ISBN 0-912524-46-4 (pbk.)

Contents

Disclaimer

This book is only considered to be a general guide. The author and publisher have neither liability nor can they be responsible to any person or entity for any misunderstanding, misuse or misapplication that would cause loss or damage of any kind, including material or personal injury, or alleged to be caused directly or indirectly by the information contained in this book.

Acknowledgements

The following is an alphabetical list of the companies who contributed information used in producing this book: A-1 Flake Ice Machine, Everpure, Inc., Filtercold Corp., Follett Corp., Henry Vogt Machine Co., Ice-O-Matic/Mile High Equipment Co., Kold-Draft/ Uniflow Mfg. Co., North Star Ice Equipment Corp., Reynold/Alco, Scotsman Commercial Ice Systems.

Special thanks to Alphi Refrigeration, Crystal Tips, Inc., and Philadelphia Wireless Technical Institute.

Dedication

This work is dedicated to my wife, Renée, whose help and patience made it all possible.

FOREWORD

Unlike many other trades, the refrigeration industry is relatively young. As an instructor teaching air conditioning and refrigeration to newcomers in the field, I was amazed by the lack of written information available to them. My distress at this lack of information was the primary factor which prompted me to write this book.

A catch-22 problem exists in the refrigeration industry. Many servicemen wish to learn ice maker servicing but, in many cases, it's just too costly for an employer. Many employers cannot afford to pair an inexperienced mechanic with an experienced one so the former can learn the basics of ice machine repair. On occasion, I have been approached by service personnel who were willing to work without wages or even pay me for the opportunity to gain experience in ice maker service.

After a careful reading of this book, apply what you learn between these covers and you will find the magic to make ice.

INTRODUCTION

Prior to the advent of mechanical refrigeration, men traveled down to the local lakes during the winter months with saws and other specialized tools. With these tools, they "harvested" the ice which had formed on the surface of the lake by cutting it into large but manageable blocks. Then they hauled these blocks back to town, coated them with sawdust for insulation and stored them in an "ice house."

Throughout the next year, these blocks were removed as needed and sold to the townspeople, who used them for their refrigeration needs. But this was a time consuming and back breaking process which was often governed by Mother Nature.

Since this process began, there have been many other factors which contributed to the need and production of artificial ice.

In the year 1890, a shortage of natural ice — the result of a very warm winter in every state except Maine and Wisconsin — caused a heavy demand for the manufacture of artificial ice.

Water pollution and the quality of ice being produced presented another unforeseen problem. Unhealthy water produces unhealthy ice. In the year 1901, an outbreak of typhoid in Chicago was blamed on contaminated natural ice. Man needed a better, healthier method for obtaining ice.

A more convenient way to get ice was developed by a man known as "The Father of Refrigeration." In 1834, Jacob Perkins took out a British patent for making artificial ice. His principle for vapor refrigeration is the same one which is used today in almost all mechanical refrigeration machines.

Ten years later, in 1844, Doctor John Gorrie invented a

machine to produce ice for use in his Apalachicola, Florida hospital. However, his work was not documented. The first documented commercial ice wasn't produced until 1856 by a man named Alexander Twinning. In these early days of artificial ice manufacture, the product was made into blocks resembling the ice removed from lakes. It was still used in what our parents and grandparents referred to as an "ice box."

The process used to form ice consisted of a large tank filled with a brine solution that was kept at a temperature somewhat lower than 32°F (0 C). Large canisters filled with water were lowered into this tank and left to freeze into solid blocks of ice. During this freezing process, air was pumped into the bottom of each of these cans. The purpose of having air bubble up through each can was to remove any air suspended in the water by agitation. If air bubbles froze in the blocks of ice, the ice appeared cloudy. Removing this suspended air improved the appearance of the ice, which was a good selling point for the manufacturer.

It usually took about twelve hours for these blocks to freeze. Once they did, they were removed individually and immersed in a tank of warm water. This allowed the ice to melt enough so that it could be removed from the can. When each can had been "harvested," it was refilled and the ice making process repeated. This method required a good deal of labor and could not be considered "automatic", as are the machines of today.

In the early 1900s, vast improvements in the refrigeration industry helped promote the manufacture of artificial ice. Some of these included the introduction of the refrigerant referred to as R-12 by the E. I. du Pont de Nemours and Company, who manufacturer and distribute this and its sister refrigerants under the tradename "Freon."

It was not until after 1918 when the Kelvinator domestic refrigerator was introduced to the public that the shape and size of manufactured ice began to change to better fit the needs of the individual user.

Today there are machines on the market that produce anywhere from fifty pounds to eighty tons of ice in twenty four hours of operation. Although ice makers come in various sizes and production capabilities, this book deals primarily with the commercial machines that produce up to (in most cases) two thousand pounds of ice per day. Ice making machines that produce over this amount are considered industrial ice makers.

Today ice is produced by many different machines and in various quantities. It has several uses and can be obtained just about anywhere. Every day ice makers produce ice for soda cooling in restaurants and fast food places. Commercial fishing boats fill up their holds every morning before going out to get the catch of the day. Ice is even used in dam and nuclear power plant construction since it can replace up to ninety percent of the water added to concrete during the mixing process to ensure even curing of large scale concrete constructions.

Ice use and production have come a long way since men hauled blocks of ice up from the lakes. These innovations have made both the manufacture of ice and servicing ice makers necessarily more involved. Due to the increasingly more sophisticated nature of commercial ice makers, this has prevented just any refrigeration technician from working on them. However, by taking time and applying the information contained in this book, proficient refrigeration service personnel should find that ice maker repair is a relatively uncomplicated craft.

SECTION 1

ICE & ITS USES

Most people do not believe that the shape of ice is very important. The shape of the ice used is or should be determined by a customer's needs. If ice is required to cool drinks, the customer is better off using cubes. On the other hand, if it is used for product packing, as in a restaurant salad bar or in a supermarket to cool a fish display case, then chipped or flaked ice is the best choice.

It is not common knowledge that flaked or crushed ice is considered less effective in cooling beverages than cubed ice. The problem is twofold. First, because of the small size of the individual pieces of ice, they melt rather quickly. When the melted ice mixes with the soda syrup in a soft drink, an undesirable watered down or two-tone taste results. The reason for the rapid melting of flaked or crushed ice is the surface area (in relationship to the mass of the individual piece of ice) is greater than that of an individual cube. The same principle applies to snow. In the winter, people shovel their walks and driveways, leaving large piles of snow off to the side. When the outdoor temperature rises, these piles last much longer than the thin blanket of snow that covers the rest of the landscape.

Although flaker ice is ineffective for cooling beverages, it is excellent for packing food products. It keeps fish and vegetables fresh in grocery stores and preserves and cools food in restaurant salad bars. Cubed ice, on the other hand, is sometimes too large to be useful in this manner. As a rule, cubes are for beverages, and flaked ice is for packing. There is one exception to this rule. Movie theater owners and operators prefer flaked ice over cubes because flaked ice spilled on the floor melts much quicker than cubed ice.

This reduces the possibility of a patron becoming injured by slipping and falling in the dark.

There are often occasions when a customer needs both cubed and flaked ice. In this instance, four solutions exist:

1. Purchase one ice maker to produce flaked ice and another one to produce cubed ice. However, this isn't always an acceptable solution because:
   - the cost of two machines may not outweigh the benefits
   - two separate bins are needed and the space required for them may not be available
2. Purchase a machine which produces both flaked and cubed ice. There are a few machines on the market capable of producing both, the Vogt ice maker for example. This type of machine automatically switches from one type of production to the other.
3. Purchase a cuber ice maker and an ice crusher (also known as an ice grinder). Then as flaked ice is required, the cubed ice can be put through the grinder and turned into flaked ice. The drawback to this process is the additional time required to produce enough flaked ice to fulfill a customer's needs.
4. Use either an extremely small cube or utilize some of the specialty cubes on the market such as the Scotsman Contour Cube which is an extremely flat cube that works well in either beverage cooling or product packing.

There are other factors, besides the shape, which make ice unsatisfactory for use in beverages. Many people do not realize that when ice is stored in bulk in a freezer, it's quality for beverage cooling becomes unsatisfactory. Most freezers are set to hold a temperature of from 0 to $-10°F$ (-18 to -23 C). Water changes into ice at $32°F$ (0 C) at sea level. Storing ice below $25°F$ (-4 C) produces supercooled ice. If this ice isn't brought to a temperature above $25°F$ (-4 C) any soda or beverage that hits the supercooled ice foams excessively. If this happens at a service bar or a fast food counter where speed is important, service time slows down considerably. If the stored ice is used for product packing, the additional cooling effect gained from supercooled ice is not substantial; this extra cooling is still only sensible heat. Remember that it takes only one Btu to change the temperature of one pound of ice one degree Fahrenheit—as long as there is no change of state. Further, 144 Btu are required to change ice at 32°F (0 C) to water at the same temperature.

Another common customer complaint results when the individual cube desired is either too large or too small to be useful. The only way to correct it is to sell the customer a completely new ice maker or change the evaporator to a smaller size cube. Both of these operations are extremely costly. In most cases, the customer will probably opt to do nothing other than change his glass or cup sizes. As one remedy, for example, Crystal Tips equips its cubers with a variable position cube size control.

Customers are concerned with color as well as size and shape. Without a doubt, cloudy ice is not as appealing as crystal clear cubes. Cloudy or milky ice is produced when the water is not moving during the freezing process and air bubbles are trapped inside. Most commercial ice makers constantly recirculate water over or onto the evaporator to avoid trapped air. Nevertheless, ice produced by these machines may still have an opaque appearance due to the impurities in the water. These impurities can affect the taste of the ice and may actually reduce the production of the machine by lengthening the cycle times. They can also damage the water circuit components, leading to costly repairs.

As problems arise, service personnel should keep in mind that the average life expectancy of an ice maker is generally considered to be about seven years. Working on a machine approaching this age often requires expensive repairs. It is probably wise to advise the customer to weigh the difference between replacing the defective components or having a brand new machine installed. With a new machine, the customer gets some sort of warranty to cover the entire unit. If the technician just replaces the defective parts, only those new items are covered and the customer has no guarantee that other worn parts in his machine won't break down the next day.

SECTION 2

WATER PROBLEMS

Water is the single most important element in an ice maker. And every machine is affected by the characteristics of the water used in the ice making process. Because water plays such a prominent role in the production of ice, it also contributes significantly to the breakdowns associated with ice maker operation.

Between sixty and eighty percent of all ice machine breakdowns are water quality related. Many times the problem can be temporarily corrected by properly cleaning and/or sanitizing the machine. However, if a customer is interested in maintaining an ice maker in proper operating condition, it is in his best interest to treat the water before it is fed into the machine. This minimizes the down-time of the machine and eliminates the need for major outside ice purchases. To treat water so it does not have an adverse effect on the ice maker, it is important to understand the different water related problems that can affect these machines.

These problems can be separated into five groups:
- lime scale
- dissolved solids
- bacteria (organic matter)
- acid water
- corrosion

LIME SCALE

The most common problem affecting ice production is scale formation. Scale is a dense coating of mineral matter—largely calcium and magnesium salts. As water temperatures cool, scale

5

precipitates and settles out on the evaporator surfaces that are exposed to water. Nearly ninety percent of scale deposits are composed of calcium (limestone) which is readily soluble in water.

When suspended in water in low concentrations, mineral salts that form scale are invisible to the human eye. However, as temperatures cool and water freezes the mineral particles "freeze-out" or remain in the unfrozen sump water—increasing in concentration. As the concentration of minerals increases, the water can no longer hold them in suspension so they precipitate out and form an opaque (white) deposit which often resembles chalk.

The quantity of dissolved calcium and magnesium salts present in water is referred to as water hardness. Hardness is measured in grains/gallon. One grain equals 17.1 parts/million (ppm). Excessive amounts of impurities and mineral salts settle out as scale and form deposits on evaporator surfaces. Scale insulates evaporator surfaces diminishing the heat transfer capability of the ice producing surface which, in turn, results in a reduction of ice making capacity. If left untreated, scale deposits can:

- build-up and eventually restrict or even clog the water distribution system
- accumulate and insulate the sump pump motor housing and cause it to run warm (in time, the motor may fail due to overheating)
- cause ice to stick to the evaporator, increasing the length of the harvest (this condition reduces overall ice production by extending the cycle times)

Scale that accumulates on the grid wires of a slab/hot-wire machine can eventually cause the wires to overheat and burn out after a period of time. Burned out and/or broken grid wires produce poor quality ice because of the lack of uniformity between individual cubes.

In the freezing chambers of flaker ice makers, scale adds extra load to the gear motor and assembly which causes these components to weaken until they eventually fail. Failures of this type are costly; owners must pay for expensive replacement parts as well as for the labor to install them.

To reduce costly repairs and minimize scale build-up, hard water must be controlled. The most common method of controlling hard water is to use a water softener. Under no circumstances should a common water softener be used in the water supply of an ice machine because most water softeners use the ion exchange method of hardness correction. The ion exchange is a chemical process which replaces impurities such as magnesium and calcium ions with harmless sodium (salt) ions. In the case of a plated evaporator, the ion exchange can contribute to raising a reverse electrolytic action which promotes pitting of the evaporator surface.

Since scale molecules are smaller than the water molecules they bond to, scale particles cannot be entirely filtered out of water. However, they can be removed through a safe chemical process. One of the most effective methods of reducing water hardness is to install a polyphosphate feeder in the water line. When installed, this feeder is set to dispense from 0.5 to 1.5 ppm of treatment chemical to reduce the problems associated with scale build-up in ice makers. The feeder chemical coats impurities in the water with a substance that hampers their ability to adhere to the surfaces of the ice maker water circuit—especially the evaporator plating. An ice machine that utilizes a polyphosphate feeder should be equipped with a mechanical system to periodically bleed-off or dump sump water to control high concentrations of chemicals and impurities in recirculated water that contribute to the scale problem. Often, local water conditions dictate the necessity and effectiveness of bleed-off. For example, areas with high water hardness may require more frequent bleed-offs than areas with only moderately hard water. Remember, if water conditions mandate frequent bleed-offs, some refrigeration loss may occur.

Alternatives for combatting scale include the use of:
- vinegar
- citric acid
- special slimicides and scale removal acids manufactured especially for ice makers

These solutions are all approved by manufacturers for use in ice makers—provided they are used according to directions and in proper dosages.

ACID WATER

Acid water contains an overabundance of carbon dioxide which tends to dissolve and form carbonic acid. There are two possible explanations for this reaction:
- decayed organic matter in the water
- air pollution from fossil fuel combustion
  (which ultimately contributes to acid rain)

Acidic water conditions may cause corrosion of the ice maker chassis and storage bin. For the most part, it is not a problem to the water circuit because most of these parts are made of plastic or are covered in some sort of non-corrosive material such as nickel, tin or chrome plating. However, in extreme cases, to neutralize acidic water a machine can have a chemical feeder installed in the water feed line to administer a dose of alkali solution such as soda ash. When dissolved in water, an alkali compound neutralizes acidic water via a chemical reaction and yields hyrdroxyl ions which precipitate out as scale that can be removed through bleed-off. The quantity of alkali material present (i.e., alkalinity) is directly related to the pH factor of the water sample. Consequently, the alkalinity factor of water has proven to be the most accurate test to determine whether a water sample has a potential scaling condition or if the water is corrosive.

In addition, if it is also necessary to chlorinate feed water, the chlorine and alkali solution can both be effectively fed by the same chemical feeder. In the event soda ash is added to neutralize the water supply, a filter must be installed down stream from the chemical feeder to prevent the solution from clogging the water circuit.

TOTAL DISSOLVED SOLIDS (TDS)

This term describes all suspended and dissolved impurities contained in water. TDS contributes to the problems caused by scale build up.

Dissolved solids may be removed by filtering with fine mesh, high quality water filters. Filters used in the ice industry can remove particles as small as one micron. Some commercial filters also include a carbon filter element which aids in removing bad tastes and odors from water.

Figure 2-1. Insurice 2000 water filtration system designed specifically for ice machines. (Courtesy, Everpure, Inc.)

ORGANIC CONTAMINATES

Bacteria, algae and slime are caused by water borne and air borne spores that grow under favorable conditions. Cigarette smoke is an excellent example of how bacteria spores are transferred to ice makers. When an ice machine is placed in a bar or restaurant which is patronized by large groups of smokers, the tobacco smoke, contaminated with bacteria from smokers, travels through the air and settles on every surface in the building. This bacteria-laden smoke finds its way into the ice maker and has the perfect spot to grow.

Bacteria, slime and algae build-up can eventually lead to reduced ice production, poor ice quality and taste. However, bacteria cannot be removed with a filter. These organic contaminates can only be eliminated if the owner of the machine can identify the problem and is shown how to treat it. Proper cleaning and sanitizing only alleviate the condition temporarily. In extremely bad cases, the addition of a chlorine feeder (installed after the solid filter bank) may be required for the supply water line.

Algae, slime and bacteria are effectively removed from water by chlorination. Chlorine added to the water in proper amounts is beneficial in that it:
- reduces growth of bacteria in the water
- inhibits the growth of air borne bacteria

However, an overdose of chlorine can:
- reduce ice quality by altering the taste of the water (too much chlorine in the freezing water)
- contribute to the erosion and deplating of evaporator surfaces due to the unbalanced water ph (too much chlorine in the water distribution system)

In most cases, sufficient chlorine is added at the pump house or well so that additional chlorination at the machine's supply water line is unnecessary. Systems connected to private wells should by all means be chlorinated if for no other reason than to prevent the possibility of disease caused by water borne bacteria.

The following information is used with the permission of the Follett Corporation.

STAINLESS STEEL & CORROSION

There are many different grades of stainless steel available, and they vary in their ability to resist corrosion. The type that is least resistant to corrosion is the group known as the "400" series stainless steel which contains chromium as its primary element. This steel is readily identifiable because it is not magnetic. The other types of stainless steel that are used commercially are more resistant to corrosion and are magnetic because they utilize chromium in combination with other metals such as nickel and manganese. The other two grades normally used are the "300" series (chromium and nickel) and the "200" series (chromium, nickel and manganese). For the most part, the two latter groups have about the same corrosion characteristics and are used interchangeably.

Commercial grades of stainless steel all tend to corrode or rust when exposed to certain chemicals or salts. One element that readily attacks stainless steel is chlorine (also most chlorine compounds such as hydrochloric acid and certain salts containing chlorine). The speed with which this corrosion occurs (rate of reaction) depends on the concentration of the chlorine and the length of exposure.

Bin Liner Rusting:

In many ice bins, a rust stain or brown deposit appears at the top of the side and rear walls of the bin liner. Other areas, such as stainless steel door back pans or exposed stainless parts inside the bin (which are not covered with ice), are also prone to rust stains. If the bin is used regularly, the lower portions of the liner walls usually stay clean due to the "washing" effect of the ice that melts and drains down the walls. The liner stains may appear more rapidly in some installations than others, depending on the water conditions and the machine's method of ice production.

Staining or rusting results from two primary sources:

- **Foreign Materials** — For example, many ice machine housings are made of painted steel. If this steel is exposed at the joint where the ice machine sits on the bin, it is prone to rust. The rust may then drip down and stain the liner walls. Particles of plain steel may also fall down into the bin and, in turn, rust.

- **Materials expelled during ice making** — Most ice makers produce clear ice by freezing-out common tap water impurities such as chlorine gases and solids. Being heavier than air, these foreign materials drop down into the bin. This may explain why stains are more noticeable on an installation where the bottom opening of the ice machine is quite large. Chlorine gas contained in the water combines with water vapor and condenses as a mild hydrochloric acid on the liner wall. Any acid above the normal ice level in the bin is not removed by the action of the ice and eventually stains the liner.

Because an ice machine is often exposed to significant quantities of potentially corrosive material, it is important to periodically clean it. Cleaning prevents stains and/or rust from pitting the stainless steel liner. The interval between cleanings depends primarily on the local water conditions and type of ice machine.

If maintained properly at regular intervals, stainless steel ice bin liners should provide many years of sanitary, trouble-free ice storage.

SECTION 3

TOOLS OF THE TRADE

When water related or any other type of problems cause a machine to break down, don't worry. The maintenance and repair of ice makers can be relatively uncomplicated—provided service personnel understand which tools are required and know how to use them. Having the right tool for the right job has always proven to make the serviceman's life a bit easier. And acquiring the correct tools for a job can be done gradually, without spending a lot of money.

The following is a basic list of tools necessary not only for servicing ice makers but also in other aspects of the refrigeration trade. Although some specialty tools are required to work on ice makers, those are identified and their use described wherever they are mentioned within the context of this book.

- Gauge manifold
- Tubing cutters, Flaring block, Swaging tool
- VOM or voltage tester
- Vacuum pump—preferably two-stage
- Pliers, Hammer—preferably lightweight ballpeen
- Screw drivers—philips and blade
- Wrenches—adjustable and standard
- Torch—acetylene, oxy-acetylene, or any type capable of producing sufficient heat for brazing
- Stop watch—to time the cycles of the ice maker. Standard practice is to time the cycle from the beginning of one harvest to the beginning of the next.
- Leak detector—Either an electronic or a halide torch. When buying a leak detector, evaluate the different types available then buy the best and most affordable one possible.

- Weight/Charging apparatus—Either an extremely accurate scale (½ ounce or better accuracy) or a charging cylinder

Every refrigeration serviceman should be aware that the use of each tool and/or instrument in the tool arsenal has the potential to create problems. Industry experts indicate that approximately ninety percent of all refrigeration failures are caused by improper installation/repair practices. Typically, these faulty repairs are caused by one of two reasons:

1. The installation mechanic neglected to read the manufacturer's installation instructions. Remember the adage: When all else fails read the instructions.
2. Total disregard for cleanliness whenever a closed refrigeration system is opened to the atmosphere.

VACUUM PUMP

This is probably the most abused tool in the refrigeration industry. Just pulling a closed system down to a reading of 30-inches on the compound gauge does not mean the system has been properly evacuated. A proper evacuation can only be accomplished with the use of a low vacuum gauge, one that is capable of reading into the "micron" range or its equivalent. A system should properly be evacuated to a reading of between 500 to 50 microns. (This is the only effective way of testing or checking the operation of a vacuum pump.) If a low vacuum gauge is not available, use the triple evacuation method as an alternative. However, only use this procedure in the event that a low vacuum gauge is unavailable. The use of triple evacuation is much more time consuming than the use of a low vacuum gauge, and other ramifications come into play such as system cleanliness and CFC emissions which have contributed to the depletion of the ozone layer.

Whenever a closed system is open to the atmosphere, it is considered good repair practice to change the filter dryer prior to performing an evacuation. This is accepted as proper procedure to ensure the complete removal of moisture from a system.

TRIPLE EVACUATION

The following is a step-by-step guide to performing a triple evacuation.

1. Evacuate the closed system down to 30-inches of mercury on the compound gauge.
2. Keep the vacuum pump connected to the system and running for at least 30 minutes.
3. Break the vacuum by adding refrigerant to the system through the service gauge manifold to a pressure of approximately 5 pounds.
4. Let the system hold this refrigerant charge for about 5 minutes. The refrigerant does not have to be the same one that operates the system. Its purpose is to soak up any moisture and contaminants that may be left in the closed system.
5. Dump this partial charge from the system after 5 minutes.
6. Evacuate again to 30-inches on the gauge.
7. Keep the vacuum pump running for another 30 minutes.
8. Break the vacuum a second time with clean refrigerant to a pressure of approximately 5 pounds.
9. Hold the system at this charge for approximately 5 minutes.
10. Dump the holding charge and evacuate the machine down to 30-inches on the compound gauge one last time and keep it there for 30 minutes.

After this procedure is performed, the ice maker is ready to be charged with the proper operating refrigerant.

WEIGHT/CHARGING APPARATUS

Some ice makers may use a TXV or another type of metering device, however, the charge is critical. Ice makers are usually small-package manufactured pieces of refrigeration equipment. The refrigerant lines are short and the components are very close together leaving little room in the system for any extra refrigerant. Being slightly over or undercharged can increase cycle times. Consequently, ice production can decrease. Longer harvest times cause reduced ice production and can likely cause numerous call-backs—until the serviceman properly resolves the problem.

It must also be understood that today the compressors in most ice makers are of the hermetic type and require a proper amount of cooling. This is determined by the amount of refrigerant returning through the suction line. In an over-charged machine an excessive amount of refrigerant tends to slug the compressor which results in bearing and valve failure. On the other hand, an under-charged system causes the compressor to overheat and eventually leads to "burn-out."

SECTION 4

FLAKER ICE MAKERS

Since modern ice makers are generally compact packaged units, their refrigerant lines are short and the components mounted to conserve space. The short tubing runs and close proximity of the components leaves little room for extra refrigerant. These machines are all basically the same and differ very little from other types of refrigeration equipment. However, no one type of ice maker is immune from problems. Flaker ice makers can be as maintenance-free or as troublesome as a cuber, or vice versa.

As discussed previously, flaked ice is mainly intended for use in product packing. Flaker ice makers can produce anywhere from 200 pounds to one ton of ice in a 24-hour period. In flaker machines, the ice making process is continuous, unlike that of a cuber which alternates between the ice making process and the harvest cycle.

Flakers can be considered mechanical ice makers. Like other mechanical ice makers, if they are not properly maintained on a regular basis, they are prone to breakdown. This is due to the wear on the moving parts. When a breakdown occurs, it is often not possible to substitute parts from one manufacturer's machine to another. It is also rare to find generic parts which work adequately to repair an ice maker.

The first look inside a flaker ice maker may be cause for some surprise. There is not much to see. Every step of the ice making process occurs inside the different components. For this reason, it is not necessary to disassemble the unit to check its operation. Rather, monitor the operation of the machine via the use of gauges, volt and amp meters and by carefully listening to the operation of the machine. (Disassembly is required, however, for periodic bearing inspections.)

17

Use extreme caution when working on an energized flaker ice maker. Do not stick anything inside of the ice discharge chute. The rotating cage or auger (the auger is a set of metal blades that rotate in close proximity to the evaporator surface) is driven by a large motor equipped with a reducing gear box. When something becomes stuck inside the chute, the motor slows down. With this reduction in speed comes an increase in torque at the output or evaporator end. Whatever object is stuck in the evaporator section while the auger is turning will likely be destroyed before the gear motor or any of the other parts fail. Be warned, in the event that a serviceman's finger or digit is stuck into the evaporator section, it will no doubt be surgically removed.

The main complaint that users have with flaked ice is that the ice produced is very wet. Scotsman has come up with a unique method of reducing the amount of water in its flaked ice by extruding the ice before depositing it in the ice storage bin. This ice is produced by the Modular Nugget Icemaker which produces ice that is classified somewhere between cubed and flaked ice.

The Scotsman machine is very well suited to ice transport systems. An ice transport system involves a flaker ice maker located in a remote area. Through the use of a moderately sized, flexible hose, the ice produced at this location is pumped to one or more separate locations. This procedure is perfect for places like a bar in a convention center where the ice usage is heavy, but there is not enough room in the area to install an adequately sized ice maker. Having an ice maker in one location and "pumping" the ice to ice service bins in another can save the customer a great deal in employee labor and lost service time.

The following describes the step-by-step operation of both the refrigeration and water circuit of flake ice makers.

REFRIGERATION CIRCUIT

Operation:
1. The compressor turns low pressure, low temperature refrigerant (gas) into high pressure, high temperature refrigerant (gas).

2. The refrigerant enters the condenser and gives off heat while it condenses from gas to liquid. (In losing heat the refrigerant changes states from a gas to a liquid because the temperature of the cooling medium, air or water, is lower than the refrigerant.)

3. The liquid refrigerant leaves the condenser and travels through the liquid line to the metering device which sprays the liquid refrigerant into the evaporator.

4. The pressure in the evaporator is lowered by the operating compressor and, because of this, the liquid refrigerant boils. (In order for the refrigerant to boil, it must pick up heat. In an ice maker, the substance from which it picks up heat is the water that comes in contact with the evaporator.)

5. The refrigerant leaves the evaporator and returns to the compressor where the process is repeated.

Remember, in order for water to change into ice, it must be reduced in temperature to 32°F (0 C) or lower. Consequently, the temperature of the evaporator surface must be cooler than the water.

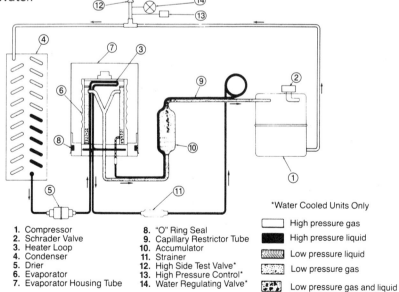

*Water Cooled Units Only

1. Compressor
2. Schrader Valve
3. Heater Loop
4. Condenser
5. Drier
6. Evaporator
7. Evaporator Housing Tube
8. "O" Ring Seal
9. Capillary Restrictor Tube
10. Accumulator
11. Strainer
12. High Side Test Valve*
13. High Pressure Control*
14. Water Regulating Valve*

☐ High pressure gas
■ High pressure liquid
▨ Low pressure liquid
▦ Low pressure gas
▤ Low pressure gas and liquid

Figure 4-1. Diagram of the closed circuit refrigeration system of a flaker ice maker. (Courtesy, Crystal Tips, Inc.)

WATER CIRCUIT

Operation:

1. In a flaker ice maker, the water enters the machine through a float valve that is something like the float assembly in a domestic toilet tank. (This valve is positioned nearly even with the top of the evaporator to keep the water level up near the ice ejection port of the evaporator cover.)

2. When the machine is turned on, the equipment and the auger motor are energized.

3. As ice forms on the evaporator surface, the rotating blades of the auger assembly scrape it off. This ice floats to the top of the evaporator section.

4. With the help of the top of the auger assembly, additional ice which is scraped off the evaporator floats up forcing the ice out through the ice ejection port.

5. Ice discharged from the ejection port enters the ice storage bin. The ice collects in the bin until it is full and the machine is shut off by either a mechanical or a thermostatic bin control.

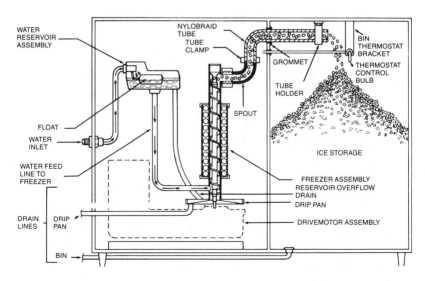

Figure 4-2. Cutaway view of a self-contained flake ice maker. (Courtesy, Scotsman Commercial Ice Systems)

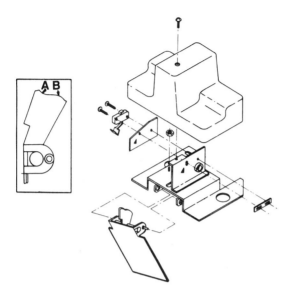

Figure 4-3. Exploded view of a mechanical bin control. (Courtesy, Crystal Tips, Inc.)

Figure 5-1. Modular cube ice maker mounted on a bin as it would appear when installed. (Courtesy, Mile High Equipment Company)

SECTION 5

CUBE ICE MAKERS

Like flakers, it is best to examine both the refrigeration and water circuit of cuber ice makers. For the purposes of this section, cubers are divided into three categories according to method of ice production:

- Vertical evaporator
- Mechanical cuber
- Slab/hot-wire grid

VERTICAL EVAPORATORS

The components of the cuber refrigeration circuit are very much the same as those in the flaker ice makers. Many manufacturers utilize an accumulator in the suction line to protect the compressor against liquid floodback during the hot-gas defrost (harvest cycle) and at the end of the harvest cycle when there is little or no load on the evaporator.

The terms hot-gas defrost cycle and harvest cycle are interchangeable. However, to prevent any confusion, the "hot gas defrost cycle" will be referred to as the "harvest cycle" throughout this book.

REFRIGERATION CIRCUIT

Operation:
1. The compressor turns low temperature, low pressure refrigerant (gas) into high temperature, high pressure refrigerant (gas).

2. The refrigerant enters the condenser at a temperature some-what higher than the cooling medium used with this machine, either air or water. Because of the temperature difference, the refrigerant loses heat to the cooling medium.
3. The refrigerant changes state from a gas to liquid.
4. The liquid refrigerant moves from the condenser through the liquid line to the metering device which sprays the liquid refrigerant into the evaporator.
5. The compressor pulls on the refrigerant, which causes low pressure in the evaporator. Because of this low pressure, the refrigerant boils. (In order for it to do so, it must pick up heat from the water that comes in contact with the evaporator.)
6. The refrigerant picks up this heat and changes state.
7. Refrigerant then moves down the suction line and returns to the compressor where the cycle repeats itself.

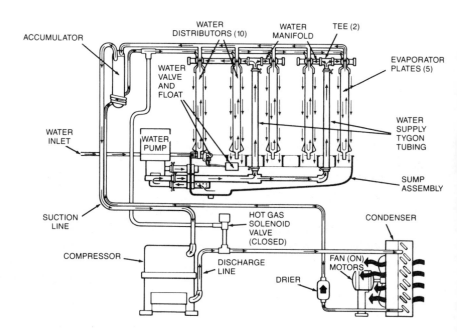

Figure 5-2. Diagram of a cube ice maker illustrating the water and refrigerant circuit during the freeze cycle. (Courtesy, Scotsman Commercial Ice Systems)

Watch the compound gauge during the refrigeration cycle. Ice grows thicker on the evaporator while the back pressure pumps down. The ice maker should go into harvest at approximately 8 pounds for an R-12 and 22 pounds for an R-502 machine. When the machine goes into harvest, a solenoid valve in the hot-gas line (which bypasses the condenser, liquid line and the metering device) opens and allows hot-gas refrigerant to pass directly into the evaporator. Hot-gas heats up the evaporator which releases ice that drops into the ice storage bin. During the harvest cycle, the back pressure should go over 40 pounds for machines using R-12 and over 65 pounds for ice makers that use R-502. After ice drops into the ice storage bin, the ice maker returns to the freeze cycle and begins producing another batch of ice.

Cuber ice makers use many different ways to set the machine into the harvest cycle and return it to the freeze cycle. One common method is to use a reverse acting pressure control to activate a finishing timer. The reverse acting pressure control is a pressure switch with contacts that close as pressure falls and has its pressure connection attached to the low-side of the refrigeration system. A finishing timer (an electronic or electro/mechanical time clock that closes a set of contacts after a predetermined amount of time) initiates the harvest cycle. However, the reverse acting pressure control cannot be used effectively to judge the proper time to set the machine into harvest because the ice thickness/back pressure relationship is a curve and the thicker the ice gets, the more coarse the pressure reading. To achieve proper ice thickness, the reverse acting pressure control is set to close at a known ice thickness and then the time necessary to finish the ice making process is judged and adjusted through a number of cycles. While adjusting the controls, the mechanic should be timing the length of each cycle with an accurate timepiece, such as a stop watch. It is easiest to measure these times if the initiation of the harvest cycle is used as the starting and stopping point of each cycle. Proper cycle times are dependant on a number of variables such as; ambient air temperature, incoming water temperature, cleanliness of the evaporator, water quality and type of refrigerant used. Use these guidelines to check cycle times:

R-12   17 to 30 minutes
R-50   27 to 25 minutes

Variations of the reverse acting pressure control utilize a reverse acting temperature control with a thermostat bulb. This bulb is mounted on the suction line to determine the temperature of the refrigerant returning to the compressor.

Remember, this book is a general guide. Whenever the instructions in this text contradict or deviate from a manufacturer's specifications, service personnel should rely on the recommendations cited in manufacturer's literature.

Occasionally the finishing timer is used to terminate the harvest cycle. In some machines, a bin door or water curtain opens every time the ice maker drops a batch of ice. When this door or water curtain opens, it hits a micro switch that momentarily opens or closes a circuit, returning the machine to the freeze cycle.

On the other hand, some machines only use a finishing timer to control the cycles. Obviously the accuracy of this process depends on the machine. If everything remains constant during the operation, the cycles will be accurate. A deviation in any of the following variables can render the cycles inaccurate: ambient air temperature, incoming water temperature, evaporator and water distribution system cleanliness, and supply water quality.

Many Manitowoc ice makers utilize a thermostat mounted on the suction line as a safety device in case all the ice melts before it has a chance to fall from the evaporator. Manitowoc calls this safety device a Thermo-disc. It is a normally closed t-stat that opens on rise at approximately 70°F (21 C). If the Thermo-disc fails in the open position, the ice maker cannot go into harvest. A simple way to check this component is to attach the probes of a volt meter to the terminals of the finishing timer printed circuit board which is connected to the Thermo-disc. If the meter shows a voltage drop (reads voltage) across the Thermo-disc, then it is open. If the Thermo-disc is open and the suction line is not warmer than 50°F (10 C), it should be replaced. If the machine has been sitting idle for some period of time and the ambient temperature is over 70°F (21 C), it is possible that the Thermo-disc is merely in the open position.

WATER CIRCUIT

The water circuit of a cuber ice maker is somewhat different from that of the flaker in that water is constantly flowing over the evaporator to ensure that very little air is frozen inside of the cubes. Ice that has air bubbles frozen in it appears cloudy, whereas ice that does not have air bubbles inside of it appears crystal clear.

The water circuit components consists of:
- water sump
- water pump
- water distribution system
- water fill valve

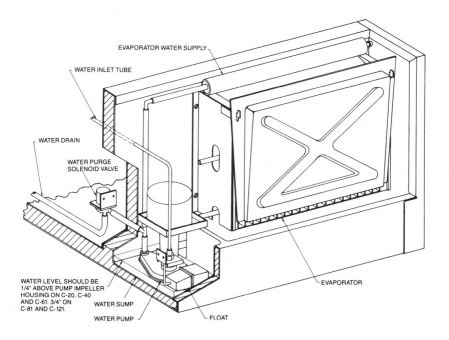

Figure 5-3. Water circulation system of a vertical evaporator ice cube maker. Note water fill valve and float. (Courtesy, Mile High Equipment Company)

Operation:

1. Turn the machine on and energize the water pump and the refrigeration equipment.
2. The sump pump pushes water through the distribution lines where it flows over the evaporator. The temperature of the evaporator surface is lower than 32°F (0 C) so, some of the water freezes to the surface of the evaporator.
3. The water that does not freeze to the surface is returned to the sump so that it can be recirculated until the end of the freezing process. The water fill valve is either a float assembly as in the flaker ice maker so a constant water level in the sump is maintained, or a solenoid valve which opens during the harvest cycle and fills the sump with sufficient water to ensure proper ice production.

Scotsman's CM 1200 C & D series, for example, uses a solenoid valve in the sump water supply line that opens during the harvest cycle to fill the sump until it overflows the sump drain. Occasionally, the strainer screen in the input side of this water valve becomes partially clogged and slows down the flow of water into the sump. This may cause the machine to prematurely go back into the freezing cycle—before the sump has sufficiently filled with water. Consequently, near the end of the freeze cycle the machine may run out of water, produce undersized cubes or not harvest properly.

VERTICAL EVAPORATOR MODELS

Vertical evaporator machines have one or more evaporators set vertically so that the water runs down them during the freezing cycle and harvest is assisted by gravity. Also, the sump pump may or may not run during harvest and the ice maker—depending on the manufacturer—drops the ice in individual sheets, separate cubes or in vertical racks or ladders.

Manitowoc & Ice-O-Matic Machines

Machines manufactured by Manitowoc and Mile High Equipment Works (Ice-O-Matic) drop ice from the evaporator as a single sheet. Proper ice size in these machines is determined by measuring what is called the "ice bridge thickness." The ice bridge is the section of ice that is formed during the freezing cycle that connects the individual cubes together. The thickness of the ice bridge should be approximately an ⅛-inch thick. This allows the sheet of ice to break into individual cubes when it enters the ice storage bin.

In older machines that have plated evaporators, it is common for the evaporator surfaces to become pitted due to reverse electrolysis, over cleaning or from the abrasive action of the water flowing over the surfaces. It is important to select cleaning solutions carefully. Some cleaners are excessively acidic and tend to promote reverse electrolysis that removes evaporator plating.

When an evaporator surface becomes pitted, ice has a tendency to stick to it. This causes the machine to take a longer time to harvest and large portions of the ice may melt before sliding off the evaporator. Increasing the ice bridge thickness (and consequently the ice sheet weight) compensates for a pitted evaporator condition and causes the ice to harvest more readily in these extended cycle situations. However, if the ice bridge thickness is increased too much, the sheets of ice may not break up into individual cubes upon entering the ice storage bin.

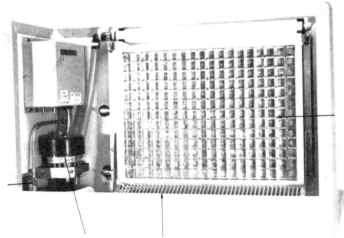

Figure 5-4. Vertical evaporator ice cube maker. Ice forms between the vertical and horizontal cube partitions. When properly formed, all cubes are connected by an ice bridge. (Courtesy, Mile High Equipment Company)

29

> **NOTE:** Do not, under any circumstance, tilt the ice maker to try to assist the harvest. This may eventually cause the compressor to fail due to a lack of lubrication.

Recently, Manitowoc introduced a new style of ice thickness sensor. It utilizes two probes which are placed vertically side-by-side in the water stream at the top left hand corner of the evaporator. A low DC voltage is applied across these two probes, and as the ice thickness increases, more water comes in contact with the probes. As the amount of the water in contact with the probes increases, the resistance to current flow between the two probes decreases until it reaches the point at which the current flow is enough for the solid state control (connected to the probes) to set the machine into harvest. One way to understand this is to visualize these two contacts as either side of an open switch. As water cascades down

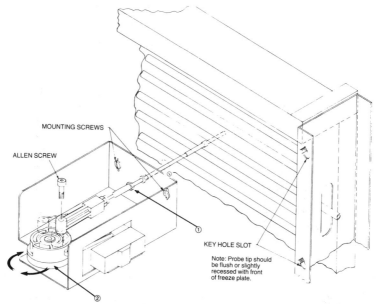

Figure 5-5. Diagram showing mounting and adjustment of Ice Probe Assist Assembly or reverse side of vertical evaporator. (Courtesy, Mile High Equipment Company)

the front of the evaporator, some of it freezes to the surface. As a layer of ice builds up, the water flowing down the evaporator is forced to flow closer and closer to the two probes. When the water is finally forced into direct contact with the probes of the ice thickness sensor, this switch closes making the circuit and sets the machine into harvest.

It is possible to initiate the harvest cycle of a Manitowoc ice maker equipped with an ice thickness sensor by shorting the two probes without damaging the sensor. In fact, Manitowoc sells a tool specifically designed to test the sensor, the Go-no-go. This tool hosts three wires with alligator clips fastened to each end. The single, uninsulated alligator clip is the common connection. The clip with the green insulator boot is the go connection, and the clip with the red insulator boot is the no-go connection. When the common and the red alligator clips are hooked across the probes of the ice thickness sensor the machine should not go into harvest. When the common and the green alligator clips are connected across the probes of the ice thickness sensor, the machine should go into harvest within six seconds. If this does not happen, replacement of the ice thickness sensor control group is necessary.

If adjustment of the ice thickness sensor is needed, it is best accomplished by using a $5/32$-inch drill bit as a feeler gauge. Insert this drill bit between the two probes of the sensor and the evaporator surface and turn the adjustment screw mounted on the sensor. To get the correct setting, adjust the sensor until it is just touches the drill bit.

The Manitowoc machine returns to the freeze cycle by means of a micro-switch that is activated by the water curtain which is a hinged plastic cover positioned over the evaporator. The curtain keeps water from splashing into the storage bin, which can melt ice, and also to insulate the evaporator from ambient temperatures.

Crystal Tips Machine

Crystal Tips uses a two position cube size control to produce either ice chips or cubes. It consists of a single-pole, double-throw (SPDT) thermostat, a heater (primary resistor) and a sheath. The sheath, which contains a thermostat capillary tube, is inserted into the ice making area of the evaporator. As ice grows on the evaporator surface, it deflects water flowing over the evaporator out towards the ice sheath. Eventually, when the ice sheath has increased sufficiently, water comes in contact with the ice size sheath. When this contact occurs, the temperature of the thermostat drops and sets the machine into harvest. During harvest, the evaporator warms up the sheath and thermostat bulb, closing the other set of contacts. The machine then returns to the freeze cycle.

The primary resistor (a heater) is attached to the sheath to offset the cooling effect of any water that splashes on the sheath during the freezing process. It continues to add heat to the ice size sheath during the harvest process to shorten its duration to some extent. Adjusting the control requires the use of a special alignment tool and no adjustment should not be attempted without it.

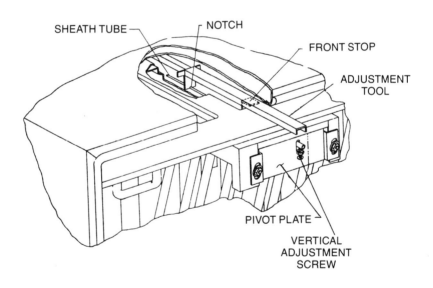

Figure 5-6. Cutaway drawing showing Ice Size Sheath location and adjustment. Note the channel like tool used for adjustment. (Courtesy, Crystal Tips, Inc.)

The adjustment procedure of the Ice Size and Harvest Control follows. (Used with permission from Crystal Tips.)

1. Remove the water pan, baffle (in envelope containing the sheath) and the front evaporator cover.
2. Insert the adjustment tool into the envelope. Position the tool so the front stop rests against the front of the envelope.
3. Vertical adjustment can be made using the vertical adjustment screw located on the pivot plate. If any horizontal adjustment is required, the nuts holding the pivot plate must be loosened. Correct adjustment is made when the sheath rests in the notch of the adjustment tool (refer to the illustration)

Recently, Crystal Tips has changed the control that adjusts the ice size. It consists of a plate with a plastic dial mounted on it. This plastic dial has a slotted off-balance hole in it that, as the dial is turned, raises and lowers the ice size sheath in the evaporator envelope. Adjustment of this new type of control is much simpler than the older type and shortens service time considerably.

Scotsman Machine

In Scotsman machines that produce the Contour Cube, ice drops from the evaporator in vertical racks or ladders. A comment made by a Scotsman representative illustrates the best way to determine the correct size of the cubes: "In the CM series of ice maker if, during harvest, the falling ice does not make a sound similar to hail hitting a roof during a storm, the ice cube size is incorrect."

To adjust the ice cube size control in the CM series machine, modify the thermostat in the ice maker control cabinet. The bulb of this thermostat is mounted on the suction line of the ice maker. This placement allows sensing of the back pressure temperature.

The adjustment instructions for a Model CM 500D which follow are used with permission from Scotsman.

Pre-start:
1. Verify that both the Master Switch and Compressor Switch are in the OFF position.

2. Supply electrical power to the ice maker by turning on the switch at the building source a minimum of 12 hours before start up to effectively warn the compressor crankcase. This step ensures that the crankcase oil is warmed sufficiently to separate refrigerant from oil. If the oil and refrigerant are not separated prior to start up, the compressor can be damaged.

WARNING: Verify the ice maker is supplied with the correct voltage and is grounded properly before beginning the 12 hour pre-start.

Start-up:

1. Remove both front panels by backing off retaining screws.
2. Verify that both toggle switches on the control box (Master ON-OFF and Compressor ON-OFF) are in the OFF position.
3. Remove control box by backing off four retaining screws.
4. Open the water supply shut-off valve.
5. Remove the stem cap from the receiver outlet (i.e., King) valve. Fully open the valve and then replace the cap.
6. Locate the switch assembly and the shaft of the timer inside the control box. Rotate the timer shaft and switch assembly clockwise until actuator arm on the micro switch drops off the outer cam and into the cam slot. (Refer to illustration of timer cam positions.) An audible click should be heard when the arm drops into the slot. In a noisy area, watch to verify that the arm drops into the slot properly.
7. Turn the Master ON-OFF toggle switch to the ON position.
8. Observe the water fill cycle which should take about three minutes to complete. As the water inlet solenoid valve opens, incoming water flows from the valve and through the tubing to fill the reservoir. Any overflow is caught and channeled through the stand pipe. Next, the timer closes the water inlet solenoid valve to complete the cycle.
9. Check to be sure the water cascades down over each cube mold and into the sump.

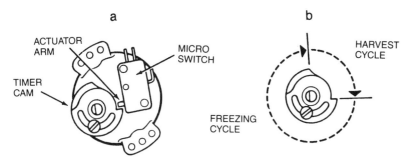

Figure 5-7. Timer cam positions: a) cam at beginning of harvest cycle, b) cam shown divided into typical freezing and harvest cycles. (Courtesy, Scotsman Commercial Ice Systems).

NOTE: Advancing the timer shaft and switch assembly through the remaining cycle and into a new harvest cycle restarts the timer and allows observation of the valve operation.

---

10. After the second cycle is complete, switch the Compressor ON-OFF toggle to the ON position. The compressor and remote condenser fan should then be operable.

11. Check for proper operation of the freezing cycle:

As the water pump operates, water moves through the two tygon tubes between evaporator plates and up to the water manifold at the top of the evaporator plates. There the water is uniformly dispensed and cascades down both sides of each evaporator plate. The water then drains back into the sump assembly to be recirculated.

Next, the ice making process starts. Note, the metal parts of the evaporator should be cold to the touch. If sufficiently cold, ice formation will begin. The tubing should become frosted at the top of the evaporator plates.

Freezing time ranges between 16 and 19 minutes in a 70°F ambient temperature. A longer time is required for temperatures above 70°F, and a shorter time if below 70°F. The average time required for a complete cycle is approximately 18 to 22 minutes.

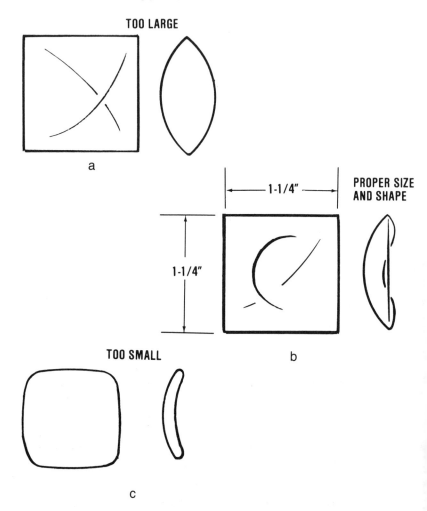

Figure 5-8. Scotsman contour cubes: a) Cube that is too large requires longer freezing cycle—may cause evaporator
freeze ups. Adjust cube size control so smaller cubes
are produced. b) Proper size and shaped cube—ice
maker operates at peak efficiency. A finely tuned system produces vertical strips of ice which break easily
when they fall. c) Cube that is too small—production
of small cubes causes excessive cycling. This condition
can cause freeze up problems due to poor harvest.
(Courtesy, Scotsman Commercial Ice Systems)

12. Observe the first ice cube harvest:

First, check the size of the contour cube. Unlike other Scotsman cubes, which are produced in a definite molded shape, contour cubes are produced in indentations and many shapes and sizes of contour cubes can result. However, only one size and shape combination is correct.

An under-charged refrigeration system may produce smaller cubes at the bottom of the evaporator plate and larger cubes at the top. To remedy this condition, recharge the system according to the nameplate (manufacturer's) specifications.

Vogt Machine

The Henry Vogt Machine Company manufactures a unique ice maker that can automatically switch to produce either cubed or flaked ice. The following is a brief outline of this machine's operation. (The ice from this machine is produced in vertical tubes.)

Operation:
1. Water is pumped from the sump to the top of the tubes.
2. As water runs down inside of the tubes, it begins to freeze to the internal tube walls.
3. At the end of the freezing cycle, the machine harvests the ice by means of a hot gas bypass solenoid. The ice, in the shape of long cylinders, begins to slip out the bottom of the evaporator.
4. The cylindrical ice slides out of the evaporator and is chopped into short pieces by the blades of an ice cutter. The cubes are then deposited into the storage bin.

The Vogt machine is capable of simultaneously producing flakes and cubes, and changeover is automatic. This is accomplished in that the direction which the ice cutter blades rotate determines whether flaked or cubed ice results. In addition, the ice maker may also be set to produce only cube or flaked ice.

Figure 5-9. Picture of the interior of a Vogt ice maker. (Courtesy, Henry Vogt Machine Company)

MECHANICAL CUBERS

Three different types of mechanical cubers are available:
- spray bar
- water plate
- honey combe

SPRAY BAR

In this type of machine, the evaporator is mounted horizontally over a mechanical spray bar. As it sprays water up against the evaporator surface, the spray bar moves either back and forth or around in circles during the freeze cycle. A portion of the water that strikes the evaporator surface freezes to it in specially shaped ice cube pockets. The rest of the water returns to the sump to be recirculated. Upon harvest, the ice drops out of the evaporator. Either the ice is helped out of the freezing chamber by the spray bar or it slides down a set of tilted bars and falls into the ice storage bin.

NOTE: Mechanical damage to the components of the spray bar assembly can occur if the water tube assembly malfunctions.

A common repair in Scotsman MC series ice makers is the replacement of the water tube assembly. After the water tube and the o-rings that seal the tube assembly wear, water can leak and flow from the sump of the top evaporator into the sump of the bottom evaporator. If this situation persists, the bottom evaporator may freeze up with an excessive amount of ice. This condition can lead to mechanical damage of the spray bar assembly components.

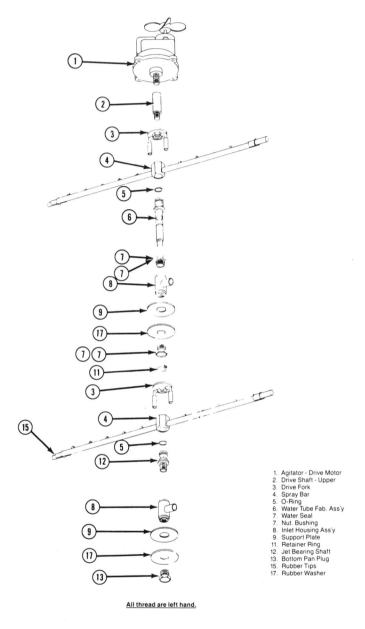

1. Agitator - Drive Motor
2. Drive Shaft - Upper
3. Drive Fork
4. Spray Bar
5. O-Ring
6. Water Tube Fab. Ass'y
7. Water Seal
7. Nut. Bushing
8. Inlet Housing Ass'y
9. Support Plate
11. Retainer Ring
12. Jet Bearing Shaft
13. Bottom Pan Plug
15. Rubber Tips
17. Rubber Washer

All thread are left hand.

Figure 5-10. Spray bar assembly for horizontal evaporator mechanical cuber. (Courtesy, Scotsman Commercial Ice Systems).

WATER PLATE

Water plate ice makers have horizontally mounted evaporators. The water plate is hinged at one end to the evaporator. The other end is controlled by a gear motor (equipped with arms) that opens and closes the hinged plate. The sump is connected to the water plate and the water distribution system is incorporated into it. The water pump is connected to the bottom

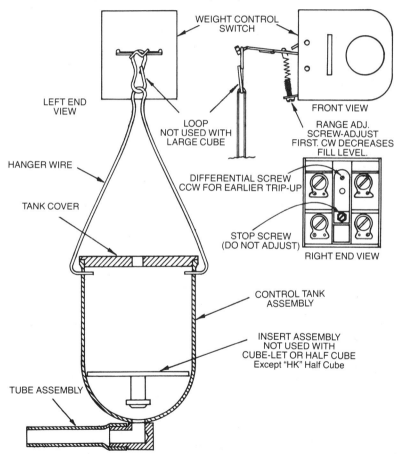

Figure 5-11. Weight control assembly for mechanical cuber utilizing a water plate. (Courtesy, Uniflow Manufacturing Company)

of the sump assembly. The water plate has two sets of holes: when it is pulled against the evaporator during the freeze cycle, water sprays through one set of holes into the ice cube cavities of the evaporator. Any water that does not freeze to the evaporator drains through the second set of holes in the plate and returns to the sump for recirculation.

Kold-Draft has an interesting approach to the filling mechanism of their water plate ice maker. Since the weight of a given amount of water is consistent, the manufacturer installed a tank in the water circuit that hangs from a spring loaded switch called a weight control. At the start of the freezing cycle, a solenoid valve in the water supply line opens and the sump and water tank fill with water. At a predetermined point (dependent upon the amount of water in the tank) the weight control trips and shuts off the water fill solenoid. As the water freezes to the evaporator, no replacement (make-up) water is supplied. The water tank gets lighter and lighter until it trips the switch in the other direction, initiating the harvest cycle.

Occasionally all the evaporator cube compartments fill with ice and the water tank and weight control still do not trip the machine into the harvest cycle. This occurs because water flow from the sump is restricted by the ice in the cube compartment. When this happens, a component called a control stream (mounted on the side of the water plate towards the front of the machine) helps rid the sump of excess water. The discharge pressure of a hydraulic water pump forces control stream water to spray over the top of the water dam and go down the drain instead of returning to the sump. This quickly reduces the water level in the sump and weight control tank, tripping the weight switch and setting the machine into harvest.

At harvest, a gear motor opens the water plate and the ice is warmed by hot-gas. This causes the ice to fall off of the evaporator as a single sheet onto the water plate, where it slides into the ice bin. A thermostat, with its bulb mounted on the suction line, activates the water plate, which closes. The system then returns to the freezing cycle.

The water plate surface of this particular type of ice maker is subject to wear because of its silicone-like coating. The coating can wear off due to: water impingement, turbulence and velocity— which all contribute to the abrasive action of the water. If any of these conditions occur, the water plate tends to freeze to the evaporator. When the water plate freezes to the evaporator, the cams of the gear motor must repeatedly force open the plate. Consequently, costly damage to the ice machine components is inevitable.

A new improvement to Kold-Draft machines has been the change-over to solid state controls. In place of the water fill by weight, Kold-Draft machines now have thermistors to sense the amount of water in the sump. Thermistors have also replaced the bin thermostat and the actuator thermostat.

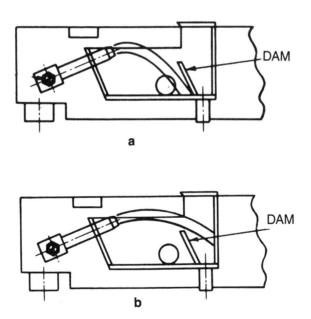

Figure 5-12. Diagram of Kold Draft "Control Stream," a) control at beginning of freeze cycle, b) control stream at end of freeze cycle. (Courtesy, Uniflow Manufacturing Company)

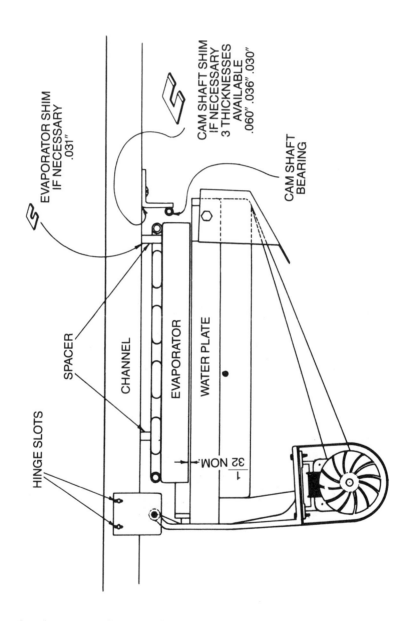

Figure 5-13. Side view of mechanical cuber utilizing a water plate. (Courtesy, Uniflow Manufacturing Company)

HONEY COMBE

This type of machine is a combination of the vertical evaporator and a mechanical cuber. Until recently, it was produced by Ice-O-Matic under the trade name Modular Cuber™.

The cube forming part of this machine is a plastic grid which is open on both sides. The evaporator is a coated plate, and both the grid and the evaporator are mounted vertically.

Operation:
1. During the freezing cycle, the plastic grid is held against the evaporator surface by a gear motor.

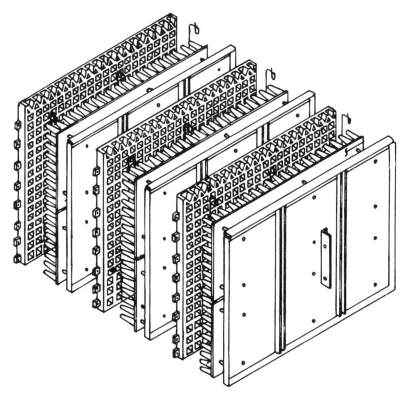

Figure 5-14. Honey combe mechanical ice cuber showing ice grid and ejector system. (Courtesy, Mile High Equipment Company)

2. Water pumped from a reservoir, located under the evaporator, to the top of the evaporator is allowed to run down over the plastic grid.
3. Once the evaporator surface has reached 30°F (−1 C), a thermostat initiates the Freeze Cycle Timer which in turn controls the operation of the machine through the completion of the freezing and harvest cycles.
4. When the ice maker goes into the harvest cycle, hot-gas is bypassed directly into the evaporator via a solenoid valve. When the evaporator has warmed sufficiently to release the ice contained by the grid, a defrost-stat actuates a gear motor.
5. The gear motor moves the plastic grid in a horizontal direction toward another plastic plate comprised of knockout pins. Each one of the pins is aligned with a corresponding hole in the grid.
6. When the grid makes contact with the knockout pins, the stationary pins force the individual cubes out.
7. The ice falls into the ice storage bin, and the grid moves back towards the evaporator plate. The cycle continues until the storage bin fills. **Note:** This machine has many moving parts and proper alignment is critical.

SLAB/HOT WIRE GRIDS

This type of machine produces ice in a "slab" shape on an evaporator plate mounted at approximately a 45° angle.
Operation:
1. Water is pumped from the sump pan to the top of the evaporator plate.
2. Water flows down over the evaporator where some of it freezes to the evaporator.
3. The water that does not freeze to the evaporator surface drops off of the end of the evaporator into the sump so that it can be recirculated.
4. After the sheet of ice has frozen to the required thickness (as determined by a thermostat) the machine goes into harvest. The bulb for this thermostat is located inside a

convex shaped container which is held by a hinged arm at a predetermined distance from the evaporator surface.

5. When the evaporator has been sufficiently heated, the ice slides down and off of the evaporator onto the hot-wire grid. The hot-wire grid is composed of two separate sets of heater wires strung in grid fashion.

6. The slab of ice lays on top of the grid which melts the ice sheet into individual cubes.

7. The cubes drop into the ice storage bin and the cycle is repeated until the bin is full.

In slab/hot-wire ice makers, some cracking of the ice slab may occur during the freezing process (prior to the machine going into harvest). This is a normal occurrence.

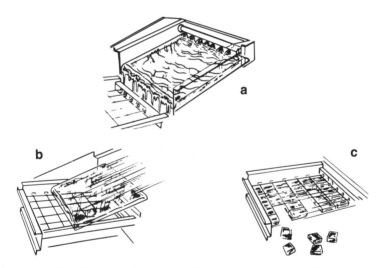

Figure 5-15. Diagram demonstrating the operation of a slab/hot wire ice cube maker. a) Water is circulated over a freezing plate. As the water freezes, minerals are frozen out and a clear sheet of ice is produced. b) When the desired thickness is reached, the ice sheet is released and slides onto a cutter grid which divides the sheet into individual cubes. c) The cubes fall into a storage bin. When the bin is full, the ice maker automatically shuts off and re-starts when more ice is needed. (Courtesy, Crystal Tips, Inc.)

Figure 6-1. Typical counter top flaker dispenser with a water dispensing valve for self-serve applications. (Courtesy, Crystal Tips, Inc.)

SECTION 6

SELF-SERVE ICE MAKERS

Manufacturers are always looking for ways to improve the operation of their machines and increase the satisfaction of their customers. Consequently, ice machines must adapt to keep up with the ever changing needs of their users. In recent years, self-serve shopping has had an impact on the ice making industry. In answer to the demand for self service, manufacturers have produced counter top ice makers and dispensers.

ICE DISPENSERS

A counter top dispenser is a storage and service machine that must be loaded with ice manually from another source. The user places an empty glass against a lever located on the front of the machine to receive ice. In most cases, this lever is wired to a micro switch which controls an electro-mechanical bin door. This switch also controls either a sweep arm, auger or screw drive assembly which moves the ice in the storage bin to the bin door whenever the individual user backs the glass away from the lever and closes the serve switch.

Typically, the only utility hookups necessary for a counter top dispenser are a 120-volt receptacle and a drain connection. A potable water connection is only required if the machine also has a water dispenser option.

ICE MAKER/DISPENSERS

A counter top ice maker/dispenser is a machine that not only stores and dispenses, but also manufacturers its own ice. The utility requirements for an ice maker/dispenser are usually water, drain and power supplies.

The ice produced by this type of machine is usually flaked, but some manufacturers' counter top ice makers create a rather large flake or nugget. At this point in time, no manufacturer has a counter top ice maker on the market that dispenses cubed ice, but that innovation is not far in the future.

The configuration of the mechanical components in a counter top machine only vary slightly from the conventional flakers described previously. In counter top machines, the ice is stored above the evaporator instead of underneath. This allows enough room for a glass or cup to be placed beneath the discharge spout.

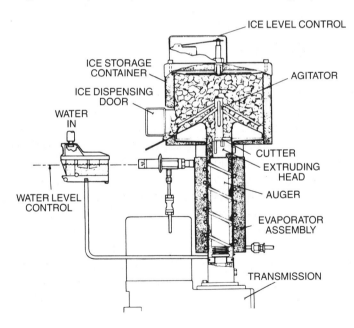

Figure 6-2. Cutaway of counter top ice maker dispenser. (Courtesy, Reynolds Products, Inc.)

Floor mounted ice dispensers usually consist of a storage bin with some means of dispensing ice either into a glass or a bucket. These machines are often very tall because the bottom of the ice storage bin must be placed at a reasonable height to be easily accessible to the user. A compatible cuber is usually placed on top of these dispensers. If the storage unit extends below the ice service door, the manufacturer provides some means of lifting the ice up from the bottom of the bin to the service door. It is important to

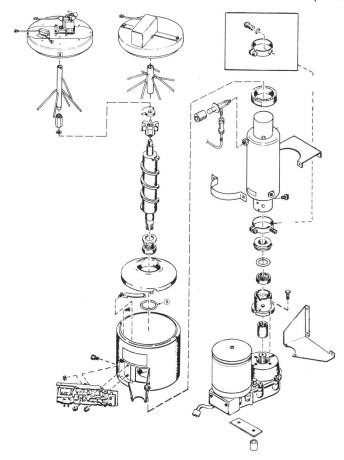

Figure 6-3. Exploded view of a counter top flaker dispenser showing ice storage/dispensing and evaporator sections. (Courtesy, Reynolds Products, Inc.)

remember that in machines of this type, (fitted with an ice maker that harvests ice in sheets) the ice bridge must be set properly to ensure the complete break up of the ice as it enters the bin. If this is not done, the mechanism for lifting the ice will not work effectively.

Many of these machines, like the counter top dispensers, also have an integral agitator bar to keep the ice from freezing into a solid mass inside the bin.

Floor mounted machines often offer a collection of options:

- **Ice bagging station** — This ice service door attachment holds and supports ice bags to allow easy filling for bulk sale. A foot pedal, which frees the operator's hands to hold, handle and tie bags, is often part of this option.
- **Low ambient kit** — Many floor mounted ice dispensers are used in "breezeway" areas in the motel industry where the outside air temperature often gets down below the normally specified operating temperature of the ice maker and dispenser. In this situation, it is necessary for some sort of artificial heat to be added to the operating station of the machines.
- **Coin and key operation** — Some owners want to restrict use of their ice dispensers either to only service their customers or to turn a profit from the ice maker. The many variations of coin and key options allows owners to discriminately limit use of their machines.
- **Decorative front and side panels** — In today's market, outward appearance and design is important. To satisfy these requirements, many machines are being designed with optional back-lighted advertising panels and different panel colors to suite the desired decor.
- **Soda heads and cold plates** — To satisfy self-serve requirements, this option is used where a larger quantity of ice is needed than is available with a counter top machine.

With the advent of these self service ice makers comes the concern for possible transmission of highly contagious and dangerous social diseases.

To minimize disease transmission, manufacturers are modifying the designs of their counter top ice makers and dispensers. Rather

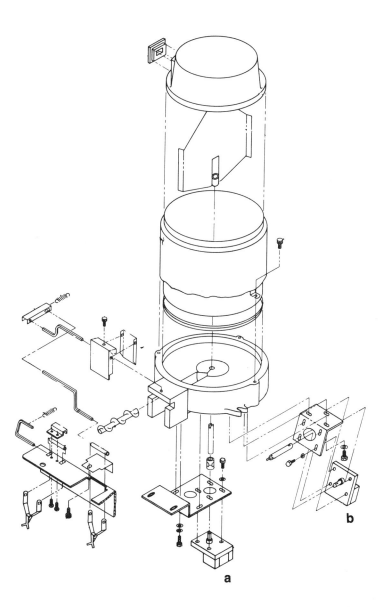

Figure 6-4. Internal view of a counter top dispenser bind assembly. Note the agitator gear motor (a) and the delivery gear motor (b). (Courtesy, Crystal Tips, Inc.)

than pushing a glass against a bar to dispense ice, customers must push a button to dispense ice. The reason for this is the fear that a person with a transmittable disease might refill his glass and transfer the germs to the push bar. The next person to use the ice dispenser/maker can potentially become contaminated by pressing the lip of his glass against the same bar.

This same concern has affected ice machines in the hotel/motel industry. Previously, the requirements for ice supplied to guests were handled by placing an ice maker with an open bin on each floor and an ice bucket in each room. Many local municipalities and local health agencies noticed an increase in the use of these open bins. However, they also noticed guests using everything from the sanitary ice buckets to trash cans to retrieve ice. To combat these practices, the laws and guidelines governing this area are gradually being changed to require the use of a closed bin type of ice storage dispenser.

SECTION 7

TYPES OF CONDENSERS

To change one pound of water at 32°F (0 C) into 1 pound of ice requires the removal of 144 British Thermal Units (Btu). A machine that produces about 600 pounds of ice in 24-hours puts out in excess of 3,600 Btu/hour or more than ⅓ of a ton per hour. All this production creates a great amount of heat which must be removed or diverted. The three most common methods for controlling heat are the use of:

- air-cooled condensers
- water-cooled condensers
- roof-top remote condensers

Ice makers installed with air-cooled condensers produce more heat than either water-cooled or remote condensers. This must be taken into consideration when selecting an ice maker for two reasons:

- it affects the size of the a/c equipment required to cool an establishment, and consequently, the cost of the entire building operation
- the heat produced by an air-cooled condenser decreases ice production – unless adequate air circulation is provided

Since air-cooled machines produce a significant amount of heat, a building housing such a unit requires an adequately sized a/c unit to compensate for the heat increase. And the larger the a/c unit required, the higher the initial purchase price – not to mention the increased operating costs the owner must incur.

In restaurants where grease tends to accumulate from cooking, another drawback of air-cooled machines becomes apparent. Any kitchen grease which splatters and lands on the surface of a

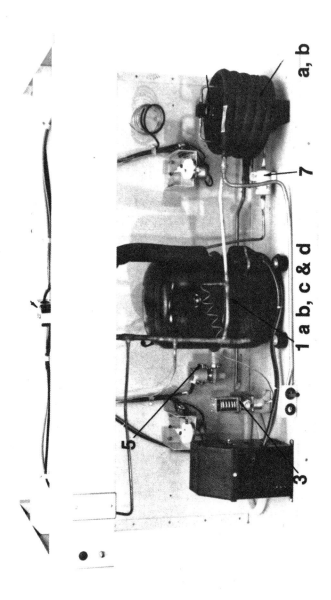

Figure 7-1. Condenser section of a water-cooled ice maker showing water-cooled condenser and water regulating valve. (Courtesy, Mile High Equipment Company)

condenser adheres like glue. Eventually the grease builds up and restricts or blocks the air flow reducing the machine's ice production. Besides reducing ice production, this condition may eventually cause the compressor to overheat and possibly fail, which can result in a costly and time consuming repair.

Finally, the additional heat out-put of an air-cooled ice maker can make an already hot kitchen unbearable. For these reasons alone, servicemen should advise their customers to switch to a roof-top remote or water condenser. Note, if the customer prefers an air-cooled ice maker, Hoshizaki produces air-cooled machines with a beneficial feature that comes as a standard item, a washable air filter. This type of filter can save a customer a good deal of money by reducing service costs incurred for merely cleaning dirty condensers.

Roof-top remote condensers provide excellent heat removal, as well as reducing the amount of equipment needed in a building. This is a benefit in that it gives the customer more room to work within. The only problem associated with remote condensers is the additional installation cost required for setting up the unit and running the wire and refrigerant lines to the roof. When installing this type of system remember:
- install the condenser away from heated areas on the roof
- route lines so no kinks develop during installation
- turn on the compressor's crankcase heater 12 hours prior to starting up the unit to extend the life of a compressor

Also note that rarely do the precharged refrigerant lines come in exactly the correct length to fit a given installation. There is usually an excess of tubing left over. Be certain to only coil any excess tubing on a horizontal plane. Coiling tubing in a vertical plane causes it to trap refrigerant oil which can eventually contribute to compressor failure brought on by a lack of lubrication.

A variation of the roof-top remote is the water-cooled, roof-top remote system manufactured by Scotsman. In this particular system, an ice maker with a water-cooled condenser is installed in the building and a closed loop, brine filled, non-evaporating water tower is placed on the roof. This machine closely resembles a refrigerant filled condenser, and results from its use are promising.

Generally, a water-cooled condenser is easy to install. However, it can cost the customer a fair sum of money to operate if the water used to cool the condenser is poured down the drain. One way to gauge the amount of water used in this type of unit is by

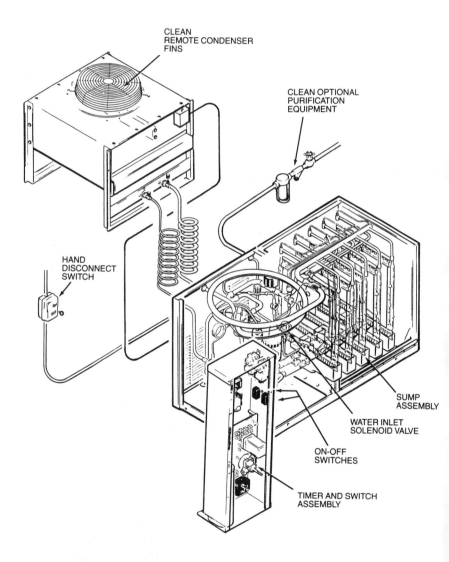

CLEAN
REMOTE CONDENSER
FINS

CLEAN OPTIONAL
PURIFICATION
EQUIPMENT

HAND
DISCONNECT
SWITCH

SUMP
ASSEMBLY

WATER INLET
SOLENOID VALVE

ON-OFF
SWITCHES

TIMER AND SWITCH
ASSEMBLY

Figure 7-2. Remote condenser ice maker. (Courtesy, Scotsman Commercial Ice Systems)

referring to the manufacturer's specification sheet. These sheets typically indicate how much water a water-cooled machine uses in 24 hours to facilitate advanced calculation of operating costs.

Determining the water usage of a particular model is an important factor when selecting what type and size machine is required for an installation. However, other variables, such as ice production, should also be considered before purchasing an ice maker.

Figure 7-3. Remote Condenser coil showing refrigerant and electrical connections. (Courtesy, Mile High Equipment Company)

SECTION 8

SIZING & SELECTING ICE MAKERS

A restaurant manager once said "You don't know how important ice is until you don't have it!" If an ice machine is too small for a specific situation or establishment, the owner or manager won't realize this until it is too late and he runs out of ice. This can be avoided if a few simple rules are followed. Just like sizing a refrigeration load, ice makers are properly sized to the heaviest load. An ice maker that produces enough ice for use in the winter may not produce enough during the summer as ice usage and the speed at which ice melts both increase in the warmer months.

Ice can be used in what may seem many different ways, but it really has only two different uses:

- beverage cooling
- product packing

BEVERAGE COOLING

To determine the ice usage for beverage cooling in a bar or restaurant, count the number of chairs in the establishment and multiply that number by 3 pounds of ice. This should cover most of the ice required to fulfill the customer's needs, unless there is an exceptionally large carry-out business. If the carry-out business is equal to or greater than 1/3 of the in store business, add 1 pound of ice for each carry-out customer. Another way to size ice needs for a carry-out establishment requires knowing in advance the size and quantity of drinks sold.

To determine the size and quantity of drinks for carry-out business, refer to the following table:

CUP SIZE (oz.)	ICE (oz.)
6	2
9	3
12	4
16	5

After establishing the number of different sized cups sold in a given day (it is better to use sales from a busy day) and multiplying that number by the quantities indicated, a fairly accurate assumption of a customer's ice needs can be determined.

If the establishment has a salad bar or some other type of display that requires ice, the amounts needed are examined separately as product packing and the amounts figured accordingly.

PRODUCT PACKING

To size an ice maker to handle product packing, it is necessary to determine the cubic feet of ice needed in 24 hours. (length × width × depth). Since the calculations are done using the foot as the standard unit of measure, the depth must be converted into feet. If the depth is less than 12-inches, divide depth required by a factor of 12 to make the conversion to feet. Remember, a cubic foot of ice weighs approximately 35 pounds, so multiply the cubic feet of space to be used for product packing by 35 to determine the customer's ice needs for a 24-hour period.

Example 1 —

A restaurant has 28 table seats, 8 stools at the bar and a salad bar that measures 6 × 3 feet with a required ice depth of 4-inches.

beverage cooling:

$$36 \text{ (chairs)} \times 3 \text{ lbs.} = 108 \text{ lbs.}$$

product packing:

$$6' \times 3' \times .33' = 5.4 \text{ ft}^3$$
$$5.4 \times 35 \text{ lbs.} = 189 \text{ lbs.}$$

Finally, add ice required for beverage cooling to ice required for product packing to determine ice requirement for a 24-hour period:

$$108 \text{ lbs.} + 189 \text{ lbs.} = 297 \text{ lbs. ice}$$

Example 2 —

A supermarket has a fish display case that is 8 feet long and 3 feet deep. They wish to set the fish in ice to a depth of 3-inches (3-inches = .25 foot).

ice requirement for 24-hours:
$$8' \times 3' \times .25' = 6 \text{ ft}^3$$
$$6' \times 35 = 210 \text{ lbs.}$$

Nursing home and hospital ice needs are calculated in much the same way as are other establishments. It is only necessary to count the number of beds and refer to the following amounts:
- Hospitals need 10 lbs. of ice for each bed.
- Nursing homes require 6 lbs. of ice per bed.

Remember, when sizing ice needs for a hospital or nursing home be sure to take into consideration other uses such as cafeterias and staff dining rooms — provided these areas do not have their own ice makers.

For churches or other places that only use ice once or twice a week it may be adequate and economical to utilize a small production machine on a large bin to fulfill an occasional need for ice. However, if this is done and two meetings or engagements are scheduled one after the other, the machine may not have time to adequately refill the bin before the start of the second engagement.

In conclusion, after the customer's needs have been determined satisfactorily, it is then necessary to consult the manufacturers' specification sheets, which list the ice production for various ice makers in 24-hour periods, to select the machine best suited for a given installation.

SECTION 9

INSTALLATION GUIDELINES

Once an appropriately sized machine has been selected, the unit must be installed. For the most part, ice maker installation is usually an uncomplicated job and can typically be handled by one or two servicemen in less than a day. Most ice makers are packaged units that consist of two components: the bin and the ice maker. Once the ice machine and bin have been installed, all that remains is to hook up the water and drain lines and then wire the electricity according to the manufacturer's instructions.

Recently, many manufacturers have introduced ice makers that utilize a remote condenser. Installing these machines requires a little more work because the condenser must be placed on the roof, and the refrigerant line and a separate electrical line are run up to the roof through a pitch pocket. Although this is more complicated than installing a package machine, it reduces the heat load in the building that results from an air-cooled condenser. In addition, the cost of city water can be reduced when utilizing a icemaker equipped with a water-cooled condenser.

In order to perform properly, ice makers must be leveled front and back. This is not only for proper ice production but also for proper compressor lubrication.

Drain lines should be pitched down in the direction of water flow approximately ¼-inch for every ten horizontal lineal feet of run. There should be a ½-inch to ¾-inch vertical gap between the machine drain line and the building sanitary receptacle. If the building drain line backs up due to a clog, this gap ensures that bacteria ridden water cannot enter the ice storage bin (through the bin drain) and contaminate the stored ice.

Installation Guidelines

Water supply lines to the machine must be large enough in diameter to supply sufficient water to the ice maker for all its needs. A common mistake made during installation is to use an under-sized water line. Since the internal walls of all water lines accumulate lime scale deposits, the smaller the line, the quicker the build-up. This eventually restricts and/or clogs water flow to the ice machine. Manufacturers' installation instructions address this topic in much more detail, pointing out potential problems and hazards. If the ice maker is water-cooled, remember to tap off of the water line ahead of the filter bank for the water to the condenser. Filtering the condenser water unnecessarily shortens the time required between filter changes and can cost the customer money.

When installing, properly support the both the filter bank and the water lines so no unnecessary stress is applied to the water connections, filters or the ice maker.

Just as the water supply lines must be adequately sized, the electric supply lines must be large enough to handle the total amperage requirements of the machine. The ice maker should have its own separate or dedicated circuit. Also mount a manual disconnect within fifty feet and in plain view of the machine. When a remote condenser is used, install a disconnect in close proximity to the condenser.

The common misconception that the National Electric Code (NEC) supercedes any local codes is not true. Consequently, contact the local municipality or the power company for pertinent information—before beginning any electrical work.

At this point it would be advantageous to consider installing the machine to facilitate future servicing. However, space limitations frequently restrict and hamper most good intentions of this nature. Inevitably what happens is the ice maker gets squeezed between other equipment wherever it fits. Then, when the unit needs servicing, the machine must be pulled out onto the floor for repair often causing quite an inconvenience for the customer.

Prior to any installation it is good practice to check the temperature range (in all seasons and conditions) of the area where the machine is to be placed. Excessively high or low temperatures can adversely affect the efficient ice maker operation.

Machines that use a bin thermostat instead of a mechanical

bin control, set in areas where the ambient temperature falls below 50°F (10 C), may not restart after ice has been removed from the bin. If the temperature drops to 32°F (0 C) or lower, damage to the supply water lines and the machine may result. Further, excessively high ambient temperatures tend to slow ice cycles, reduce ice production and gradually cause the compressor to overheat.

SECTION 10

ICE MAKER SERVICE

At one time, many believed cleaning ice makers on a regular basis prevented them from breaking down or malfunctioning. Now, manufacturers suggest the opposite. They advise only cleaning machines when required because virtually all ice maker cleaning solutions are acid based.

The base metal used in most evaporators is copper. However, if copper comes in contact with the water and ice during the freezing process, a chemical reaction takes place and copper oxide is produced. Since copper oxide is very hazardous to human health, the copper evaporator base metal must be plated with another substance to prevent or inhibit chemical reactions which may taint ice and make it unsuitable for human consumption. Overcleaning with caustic products can cause pitting or deplating of metallic (commonly tin, chrome or nickel) evaporator surfaces.

To prevent pitting, some manufacturers have even gone to the length of resurfacing their evaporators with other types of non-metallic substances, such as plastic, which are not prone to corrode easily due to water conditions.

When it does become necessary to clean an ice maker, rarely should it be done more than once a year. However, regular sanitizing of the machine is highly recommended to reduce damage to the evaporator surfaces.

CLEANING

Copper oxide isn't the only harmful substance which can occur in ice makers. Many of the chemicals used to clean ice makers are dangerous if consumed internally. Because of the nature of some machines it may be necessary to remove the ice from the ice storage bin so it does not become contaminated by cleaning solution. If any ice inadvertently becomes contaminated by the solution, there is no recourse but to discard all of the ice.

CUBER CLEANING

The following instructions for cleaning a cuber should serve as a general guideline and is used with the permission of Crystal Tips, Inc.

Ice Maker Cleaning:
1. Add approximately 10 ounces of manufacturer approved cleaning solution to the water in the sump area. In cases of extremely advanced mineral build-up, a 50% solution of citric acid may be used prior to normal cleaning.

CAUTION: Wear eye protection and take care when using acid. Follow package instructions and heed precautions noted on the container.

---

2. Switch water pump to the "Manual" position so pump circulates water without operating the compressor. Allow cleaning solution to circulate for approximately 10 to 20 minutes or until system is clean.
3. Switch pump to "Auto" position, and remove drain elbow to release water. (Note position of drain elbow before removing so it can be replaced in the same position.)
4. Remove water pan and check for cleanliness. Water pan holes cannot be restricted — clear if necessary.
5. Replace drain elbow and allow sump area to refill. Activate water pump for approximately 5 minutes, then turn pump off and drain water.

NOTE: Replace drain elbow in position to obtain desired purge.

Ice Storage Area Cleaning:
1. Remove all ice from bin.
2. Clean the storage bin with solution of 1 ounce of recommended cleaner per 1 gallon of water.
3. Flush bin thoroughly with fresh water.

The ice rack deflectors and water distributor pan may be removed and cleaned separately if required. Be sure water supply to unit is ON and unit switch is ON before leaving units. Verify that no water overflows the drain elbow during freeze cycle.

FLAKER CLEANING

The following instructions for cleaning a flaker should serve as a general guideline and is used with the permission of Scotsman Commercial Ice Systems.

Ice Maker Cleaning:
1. Remove retaining screws and the front panel.
2. Move the manual ON-OFF toggle switch (on front of the control box) to the OFF position.
3. Remove all ice from the ice storage bin.
4. Close water supply shut-off valve.
5. Disconnect the tube between the water reservoir and the bottom of the freezer assembly. Drain all water from the reservoir and tube. Re-connect the tube.
6. Prepare (Scotsman) cleaning solution:
   - MF-400: mix 4 oz. of ice machine cleaner with 1 qt. hot water
   - MF-700: mix 6 oz. of ice machine cleaner with 1.5 qts. hot water
   - MF-900: mix 8 oz. of ice machine cleaner with 2 qts. hot water

> **WARNING:** Many cleaners contain phosphoric and hydroxyacetic acids. These compounds are corrosive and may cause severe burns. If swallowed, DO NOT induce vomiting — drink large amounts of water or milk. Call physician immediately. In case of external contact flush thoroughly with water. KEEP OUT OF REACH OF CHILDREN.

7. Remove the cover to the water reservoir.
8. Slowly pour the cleaning solution into the water reservoir.
9. Move the manual ON-OFF toggle switch (front of the control box) to the ON position.
10. Continue to slowly pour cleaning solution into the water reservoir. Maintain level just below the reservoir overflow.
11. Continue ice making using the cleaning solution until all of the solution is used up and the water reservoir is almost empty.

> **WARNING:** DO NOT allow the ice maker to operate with an empty reservoir.

12. Move the manual ON-OFF toggle switch (front of control box) to the OFF position.
13. Wash and rinse the water reservoir.
14. Open the water supply shut-off valve.
15. Move the manual ON-OFF toggle switch (front of control box) to the ON position.
16. Continue ice making for at least 15 minutes to flush out any cleaning solution. Check ice for acidic taste, and continue ice making until ice tastes "sweet."
17. Move the manual ON-OFF toggle switch (front of control box) to the OFF position.
18. Remove all ice from the ice storage bin.
19. Add hot water to the ice storage bin. Thoroughly wash and rinse all surfaces within the bin.
20. Flaker and bin are ready for continued operation.

> **CAUTION:** Properly dispose of ice produced from the cleaning solution. It cannot be used for human consumption. Be sure none remains in the bin.

It is not always necessary to use the exact ice machine cleaner specified by the manufacturer. However, it is important to investigate the compatibility of the desired cleaner with the machine to be cleaned. It is possible to damage the evaporator coating if an unsuitable cleaner is used. Some common over-the-counter ice machine cleaners include:

- Lime-A-Way — Economics Laboratory
- Nickel Safe — Calgon
- Boss Brand Milk Stone Cleaner — Northern Laboratories

As previously indicated, ice makers need not be cleaned on a regular basis. Rather, they should be sanitized regularly. They should also be sanitized after the machine has been cleaned. After flushing the cleaning solution from the water circuit, add about one teaspoon of sodium hypochlorite (chlorine bleach) to a gallon of water. Put solution into sump and circulate it through the water circuit of the ice maker for approximately 5 minutes, then drain and flush the system. Unit is then ready for continuous operation.

ICE BIN LINER CLEANING

An ice machine is constantly exposed to potentially corrosive water conditions. Consequently, it is important to periodically clean the bin liner. Cleaning prevents stains and/or rust from pitting the stainless steel liner. The interval between cleanings depends primarily on the local water conditions and the type of ice machine — it may only be necessary every 3 to 6 months.

Bin Liner Cleaning:

Use the general guidelines that follow when cleaning stainless bin liners (information used with permission from Armco Steel Corp. and the Follett Corp.).

- **General Cleaning** — For light staining, remove by washing with ordinary cleaning powder such as Bon-Ami or Copper-Glo and water. (Do not use cleaners that contain bleaching agents — most of these are chlorine compounds.) After cleaning, thoroughly rinse liner with clear water.

> **NOTE:** It may be necessary to use stainless steel wool to remove stubborn stains. DO NOT USE plain steel wool. The steel particles become embedded in the liner and actually cause serious, additional rusting.

- **Cleaning Heavy Deposits**—If the liner has not been cleaned for a long time and heavy deposits and pitting are apparent, use of a chemical cleaner may be required. After using any cleaner, wash the bin liner thoroughly with soap and water. The following is a list of several recommended cleaners:
  - Oakite No. 33—Oakite Products, Inc., 50 Valley Rd., Berkeley Heights, NJ 07922
  - Texo #12—Texo Corp., 2801 Highland Ave., Norwood, OH 45212
  - Metalprep No. 10—Nelson Chemical Co., 12345 Schaefer Highway, Detroit, MI 48227
  - Dilac—Diverse Corp., 100 W. Monroe St., Chicago, IL 60603

Bin Liner Stain Protection:

If the stainless steel in an installation has been cleaned several times but the stains frequently reoccur, rejuvenate the surface to restore the characteristics of stainless steel that best prevent corrosion. The following rejuvenation process provides maximum corrosion resistance.

- First, clean the liner and thoroughly rinse with water.
- Apply a nitric acid solution of two parts water to one part nitric acid (by volume) by swabbing on the liner surface.
- Allow to stand for about 30 minutes.
- After half an hour, rinse the liner with clean water.

> **NOTE:** Always pour acid slowly into water. The reverse procedure can produce a hazardous chemical reaction.

If maintained properly at regular intervals, stainless steel ice bin liners should provide many years of sanitary, trouble-free ice storage.

GENERAL SERVICE

When servicing an ice maker, the process is easier if the serviceman observes the operation of the problem machine firsthand. By observing the machine, he can see for himself the customer's complaint and any other malfunctions which may stem from the problem. A common mistake made by mechanics is to adjust or change a component before the actual problem has been properly diagnosed. It can not be emphasized strongly enough that any changes made before the problem has been diagnosed only complicates and lengthens the time necessary to repair the machine. If the problem is mechanical, the solution should be obvious — either component replacement or adjustment. If the problem is electrical in nature, all the serviceman needs to remember is: every electrical problem can be placed in one of three categories:

- open circuits
- short circuits
- no supply voltage

If the machine has a thermostatic expansion valve (TXV), and the superheat needs checking, it may be difficult to achieve proper readings due to the nature of the machine's operation. This difficulty results from the machine going into harvest shortly after the metering device begins to balance.

Since an ice maker can be considered a low or medium temperature refrigeration machine, the superheat setting of the TXV falls somewhere within the range of 3-to-8 degrees — depending on manufacturer. Usually a superheat of approximately 6 degrees suffices.

In almost all ice makers the TXV and other refrigerant control parts are designated oem (original equipment manufacturer) and cannot be replaced with off-the-shelf components.

Remember one point when working on vertical evaporator ice makers, if the machine is short of refrigerant, the cubes produced on the upper section of the evaporator are much smaller than the cubes at the lower end. Sometimes, no ice forms at the top at all.

FLAKER SERVICE

In the past, flaker ice makers got a bad rap because they were thought unreliable. Consider just how much an ice maker runs every year (comparable to driving a car 300,000 miles/year). Next, examine how much service the machine gets during that same period of time. When considering these facts, it is hard to understand why flakers have gotten such a poor reputation.

Read service manuals carefully. Most flaker ice maker manufacturers recommend that the evaporator section be disassembled periodically and the bearing surfaces checked for wear and replaced if necessary. Service problems in these machines originate because this procedure is not done often enough. If these expensive, precision crafted machines are expected to perform efficiently for a long period of time, they must be opened up and the bearing surfaces checked for wear regularly. For the best results, inspect the bearings twice a year, and not less than once. If not done, the machines tend to self destruct from the inside. No one notices worn or bad bearings until it is too late to correct subsequent damage.

AFTERWORD

Bell Laboratories developed the transistor in the mid 1950's. Since then, the ice making industry has significantly improved its products with the use of semiconductors. The electronic age provided great innovations for the refrigeration industry. At the same token, however, it has also created apprehension among service personnel. Apparently many mechanics fear new ideas or procedures because they simply don't understand them — even if, in the long run, these methods can save time and money.

The electronic controls used in ice makers today are more accurate and reliable than the electro/mechanical components they are replacing. By using electronic circuitry, manufacturers have the capability to fine tune machines to obtain optimum performance. They have not, as many people are inclined to believe, made the machines more complicated to troubleshoot and repair. And it is not necessary to be an electronics genius in order to keep these machines in proper working order.

INDEX

Index

SPECIALIZE IN CASCADE SERVICING

Expand Your Service Skills to Include the Lucrative Field of Cascade Service.

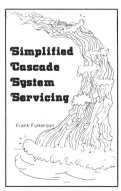

Simplified Cascade System Servicing

Frank Fulkerson

96 pages • $21.95

Cascade system servicing is not for beginners. However, if you have a solid working knowledge of refrigeration servicing, *Simplified Cascade System Servicing* shows you what you need to know to take the mystery out of servicing low temperature systems. It explains in detail the tools required and describes the service procedures used on typical cascade configurations. In addition, you'll learn to identify the various cascade configurations and how to service each one.

With this comprehensive guide to cascade servicing, you'll experience little difficulty in troubleshooting and servicing cascade system units of 25 cubic feet (1 horsepower) or less.

BNP Business News Publishing Company
P.O. Box 2600, Troy, MI 48007